If I We[...]

by Liza Charlesworth

ISBN: 978-1-338-78291-2
Illustrated by Raffaella Bolaffio
Copyright © 2021 by Liza Charlesworth. All rights reserved.
Published by Scholastic Inc., 557 Broadway, New York, NY 10012

10 9 8 7 6 5 4 3 2 1   68   21 22 23 24 25 26 27/0

Printed in Jiaxing, China. First printing, June 2021.

If I were tiny,
I could creep with a ladybug.
Creep, creep!

2

If I were tiny,
I could wiggle with a worm.
Wiggle, wiggle!

3

If I were tiny,
I could climb with a caterpillar.
Climb, climb!

4

If I were tiny,
I could slide with a snail.
Slide, slide!

If I were tiny,
I could hop with a grasshopper.
Hop, hop!

If I were tiny,
I could fly with a butterfly.
Fly, fly!

7

If I were tiny,
I could spin with a spider.
Spin, spin!

8